ANNOTATED TEACHER'S EDITION
Laboratory Manual

EXPLORING THE UNIVERSE

Prentice Hall
Englewood Cliffs, New Jersey
Needham, Massachusetts

D1529661

Laboratory Manual
Annotated Teacher's Edition

PRENTICE HALL SCIENCE
Exploring the Universe

© 1993 by Prentice-Hall, Inc., Englewood Cliffs, New Jersey 07632.
All rights reserved. Printed in the United States of America.

ISBN 0-13-985839-3

13 14 15   99 98 97 96

Prentice Hall
A Division of Simon & Schuster
Englewood Cliffs, New Jersey 07632

Contents

Overview of the Laboratory Manual

Science is an exciting area of study for the middle school and junior high-school student, and the *Prentice Hall Science Laboratory Manual* helps bring forth this excitement through a variety of activities that are interesting and informative. The *Laboratory Manual* consists of Laboratory Investigations directly correlated to the information presented in each chapter of the *Prentice Hall Science* textbook. The varied investigations and activities review information presented in each chapter and reinforce key concepts and scientific terms in an enjoyable and creative manner.

Thus, the *Laboratory Manual* is a companion text for your students, designed to help you in the teaching of the text material. This Annotated Teacher's Edition provides all the information needed to help you perform these investigations and activities with your students. It features answers to all Laboratory Investigations, annotations for general laboratory preparations, descriptions of the annotations in the Annotated Teacher's Edition, guidelines for laboratory safety, guidelines for the use and care of animals, a comprehensive laboratory materials and equipment list, and addresses of suppliers of laboratory materials and equipment.

The *Laboratory Manual* contains only Laboratory Investigations that require a minimum of materials and equipment and that can be performed without an elaborate laboratory facility. Most equipment used in the investigations should be readily available at the school or can easily be obtained locally or through a supply house at minimal cost. In addition, the Laboratory Investigations require a minimum of preparation by the teacher, and most can be completed within a single class period.

It is strongly suggested that students be required to read the appropriate Laboratory Investigation one day prior to performing it in the laboratory. Furthermore, it is suggested that the students be asked to provide hypotheses to each problem presented in the Laboratory Investigation. You may want to write these hypotheses on the board before beginning the investigation. Then, after the students complete the investigation, go back and analyze each hypothesis. Make sure students realize that they are not being graded on their suggested hypotheses. Even scientists may discard a hypothesis after the data have been analyzed.

LABORATORY INVESTIGATION FORMAT

Each Laboratory Investigation is developed to strengthen the student's laboratory procedures, use of the scientific method, and problem-solving skills. The purpose of the Laboratory Investigations is also to provide a practical application of the material presented in the student textbook. The easy-to-follow format of each Laboratory Investigation allows the students to complete the investigations on their own, perhaps after an overview and brief explanation from you. This allows you to provide the necessary help to those individuals or groups of students who require teacher assistance. Each Laboratory Investigation is organized in the following manner.

Background Information

An overview is presented at the beginning of each Laboratory Investigation. This overview relates the Laboratory Investigation to a specific key concept presented in the student text or provides background information that the student will need in order to complete the lab.

Problem

Each Laboratory Investigation challenges the student by introducing a problem in the form of a question. Upon successful completion of the Laboratory Investigation, the student should be able to answer the initial question.

Materials

Each Laboratory Investigation contains a list of materials necessary to complete the lab. The quantity of materials necessary for each exercise has been designed for groups of students or an entire class. In general, groups of six students work best. A comprehensive alphabetical listing of necessary equipment and materials can be found on page T–13 of this Annotated Teacher's Edition.

Procedure

An easy-to-follow, step-by-step outline provides details necessary for the successful completion of the Laboratory Investigation by the students. In many of the Laboratory Investigations, drawings are included to help the students as they complete the lab.

Safety symbols are included next to those steps in the Procedure that require students to follow specific safety precautions. Students should be reminded that a safety symbol alerts them to follow appropriate safety precautions for that particular step in the procedure as well as in all following steps. For example, the first time an open flame is used, students will see the symbol of the open flame. Students should put on safety goggles for that particular step and continue to wear them throughout the investigation unless instructed to remove them.

Observations

In keeping with the traditional scientific method, Observations are asked for after the Procedure in each investigation. Observations often include filling in data tables and graphs, as well as answering general questions.

Analysis and Conclusions

Using observations and knowledge gained from reading the appropriate chapter in the textbook, students are asked to draw conclusions. Analysis and Conclusions allow students to tie together the Problem, Procedure, and Observations comprising the investigation they have performed.

Critical Thinking and Application

This section encourages students to use critical-thinking skills to answer a variety of questions based on the Laboratory Investigation and their textbook reading. Many questions emphasize possible applications of the experiment just performed and allow students to tie the investigation to real-life situations they may face or to situations a scientist might face.

© Prentice-Hall, Inc.

Going Further

Each Laboratory Investigation concludes with a section entitled Going Further. This section provides students with additional activities to investigate, which may be used as enrichment activities, supplementary activities, or alternative activities. Complete instructions for performing the additional activities are included so that individual students can perform the activities without additional teacher help.

Safety Symbols

On page 4 are several safety precaution symbols. A short paragraph describes what each symbol means and the safety precautions to take when the symbol appears in a Laboratory Investigation. These symbols immediately alert students to the need for special safety precautions. It is suggested that you make sure students are aware of the meaning of each symbol before starting any Laboratory Investigation.

Teacher Annotations

This Annotated Teacher's Edition allows the teacher the convenience of immediate reference to answers, suggestions, and additional instructions or precautions for the Laboratory Investigations provided in the *Laboratory Manual*. The annotations are printed in red on the pages corresponding to the student pages.

The Annotations provided for the Laboratory Investigation questions are

1. Specific objective answers, such as those provided in Observations, Analyses and Conclusions, and Critical Thinking and Application.
2. Anticipated student answers based on varied student data where there is an expected response.
3. Subjective answers to those questions that may provide a variety of responses. These will be marked by the statement "Answers will vary." The teacher should look for a logical response based on the observations and data collected by the students during the investigation.

Guidelines for Laboratory Safety

Safety should be an integral part of the planning, preparation, and implementation of a laboratory program. Both the teacher and the student are responsible for creating and maintaining an enjoyable, instructional, and safe environment in the laboratory.

GENERAL SAFETY CONSIDERATIONS

Emphasis on proper safety precautions for each Laboratory Investigation is an essential part of any pre-laboratory discussion. Prior to each investigation, demonstrate the proper use of the required equipment. Demonstrate any potentially hazardous procedure used in that investigation. Always wear the required safety protective devices during the demonstrations and the investigations. If students are required to wear safety goggles, you and any visitors to the class must also wear them.

During an investigation, move about the laboratory to keep a constant watch for potentially dangerous situations. Behavior that is inappropriate to a laboratory situation should be curtailed immediately. Wild play and practical jokes are forbidden in the laboratory. Once students realize that the practice of safety is a required part of the course, they will accept a serious approach to laboratory work.

Any Laboratory Investigation a student performs should have your prior approval. Students should never work in the laboratory without adult supervision. At the conclusion of the investigation, cleanup should follow authorized guidelines for waste disposal. The laboratory should be restored to a safe condition for the next class.

CLASSROOM ORGANIZATION

Furniture and equipment in the laboratory should be arranged to minimize accidents. Assign students to laboratory stations. Each station should be equipped with a flat-topped table and laboratory bench. Do not use desks with slanted tops. Provide several locations where students can obtain needed supplies. Control traffic flow in the room to prevent collisions between students who are carrying or handling equipment. Tell students to leave their personal property in a designated location, away from the laboratory stations. Do not use the floor and benches for storage areas. Stress that good housekeeping is important in maintaining safe laboratory conditions. Students should keep all laboratory work areas clean. Unnecessary papers, books, and equipment should be removed from working areas.

Be sure that water faucets, hot plates, gas outlets, and alcohol or Bunsen burners are turned off when not in use.

SAFETY EQUIPMENT

Any classroom where Laboratory Investigations are performed should contain at least one of each of the following pieces of safety equipment: (1) fire extinguisher, (2) fire blanket, (3) fire alarm, (4) phone or intercom to the office, (5) eyewash station, (6) safety shower, (7) safety hood, and (8) first-aid kit. If any of these basic pieces of safety equipment are not available, you may need to modify your laboratory program until the situation is remedied.

Make sure students know the location and proper use of all safety equipment. Where appropriate and practical, have students handle or operate the equipment so that they become familiar with it. Make sure all safety equipment is in good working order. All malfunctions should be promptly reported in writing to the proper school or district administrator.

Fire equipment At the beginning of the school year, you may wish to give each student the opportunity to actually operate a fire extinguisher, as the sound and action of a CO_2 fire extinguisher can be quite alarming to those who have never used one. You may also want to have students practice smothering imaginary flames on one another with the fire blanket.

Eyewash station The eyewash station should be used if chemicals are splashed onto the face or eyes. The exposed area should be left in the running water for five to ten minutes.

Safety shower The shower is used when chemicals have been spilled on a student's body or clothing. The student should stand under the shower until the chemical is completely diluted. Have a bathrobe or some type of replacement clothing handy in case the student's clothing is so badly contaminated that it must be removed.

You may want to set up one or two spill kits in your laboratory. The contents of a spill kit are used to neutralize chemicals such as acids and bases so that they can be cleaned up more easily. Baking soda (sodium bicarbonate) can be used to neutralize acids. Vinegar (acetic acid) can be used

© Prentice-Hall, Inc.

to neutralize bases. Commercial spill kits for acids, bases, and a number of other chemicals are available from supply houses.

Safety hood Use a safety hood whenever students are working with volatile or noxious chemicals. Make sure that the room is well ventilated when students are using any kind of chemicals or are working with preserved specimens. Warn students of the flammability and toxicity of various chemicals.

First-aid kit A typical first-aid kit contains an assortment of antiseptics, bandages, gauze pads, and scissors. Most also contain simple instructions for use. Be sure to read the instructions if you are not familiar with basic first-aid procedures. A first-aid kit should be taken on all field trips. For field trips, you may wish to add such items as a bee-sting kit, meat tenderizer, tweezers, and calamine lotion. Do not dispense medication (including aspirin)

CLEANUP

Before beginning an investigation, instruct students in the proper cleanup procedures. Mark certain containers for the disposal of wastes and the collection of soiled glassware and equipment. Have students dispose of broken glassware in a separate trash container. Before the end of the laboratory period, have students unplug microscopes and other pieces of equipment and put them away in their proper location. Have students wash glassware, wipe up spills, and do whatever else is necessary to clean up their work area. At the conclusion of the Laboratory Investigation, the room should be restored to a clean and safe condition for the next class. You may wish to institute a policy of not dismissing the class until the laboratory area meets with your approval.

PREPARATIONS AND THE STORAGE ROOM

Reagents stored in the stockroom should be clearly labeled and stored safely. Take inventory of reagents frequently and keep up-to-date records of their use. Check local and state regulations for maximum permissible amounts of reagents allowed in school. In case of fire or vandalism, inform the authorities of possible hazards to the community. Keep all chemicals in a locked storage area that is accessible only to you or individuals under your direct supervision.

Some chemicals are incompatible and should be stored separately. For suggested shelf-storage-patterns, refer to *School Science Laboratories: A Guide to Some Hazardous Substances,* U.S. Product Safety Commission, Washington, DC, 1984. This publication may be obtained from your state science supervisor or the U.S. Consumer Product Safety Commission, Room 412—EX-O, Washington, DC 20207. Check local and state laws for regulations on storage of flammable liquids. The National Fire Protection Association recommends that flammable liquids be stored in vented, flame-resistant cabinets. Store large containers near floor level. Make sure that storage shelves have a raised lip at the front to prevent containers from sliding forward.

HAZARDOUS MATERIALS

Some reagents can be explosive and should not be on the premises. If found, they should be removed by trained fire or police bomb squads or by other qualified officials.

Known carcinogens and probable carcinogens have frequently been found in stockrooms and should be removed by health authorities or a licensed commercial company. If you have doubts about the hazards of any reagent in the stockroom, contact an appropriate agency (NIOSH or a local health agency).

Known carcinogens commonly found in school science laboratories include the following:

arsenic powder	formaldehyde
arsenic trichloride	lead arsenate
arsenic pentoxide	benzene
arsenic trioxide	chromium powder
asbestos	sodium arsenate
benzidine	

Possible carcinogens include the following:

acrylonitrile	cadmium powder
cadmium chloride	cadmium sulfate
carbon tetrachloride	chloroform
ethylene oxide	nickel powder

Exercise great care in using refrigerators. Never store flammable liquids in a refrigerator unless it is explosion-proof. Do not store food where microbial cultures are stored. Clean refrigerators frequently and safely discard old material.

LABORATORY GLASSWARE

Probably the most common school laboratory accidents involve cuts from chipped or broken glassware and burns from hot glassware. Discard any glassware that has a crack or chip. Use only borosilicate glassware. Fire-polish the ends of glass tubing. Allow hot glassware to cool on a hot pad for several minutes before picking it up. If an accident should happen, first aid for minor cuts and burns is immersion in cool running water. For cuts that are bleeding heavily, apply pressure with folded toweling or gauze. Call a health professional immediately.

To insert glass tubing into a stopper, lubricate the stopper hole and the tubing. Wrap the tubing in several layers of toweling and gently work the tubing into the stopper, using a twisting motion and keeping the hands as close together as possible. Wear heavy gloves. Remove the tubing in the same manner as soon as possible. Tubing that is stuck is nearly impossible to remove without cutting the stopper.

To avoid unwanted cultures, clean glassware frequently by using laboratory detergent. Most deposits can be removed with dilute hydrochloric acid or sodium hydroxide solution. Do not permit students to eat or drink from laboratory glassware.

Measuring small amounts of liquids with pipettes is common in investigations. But never pipette by mouth. Use rubber suction bulbs designed for use with pipettes or pipette fillers.

SAFETY PROCEDURES WITH MICROBIAL CULTURES

Never culture pathogenic bacteria. However, treat all bacterial cultures as if they are pathogenic. Firmly seal with clear tape any bacterial plates that are used for student inspection. For sterilization, use a high-temperature gas flame rather than an alcohol burner or candle flame.

Cultures should be killed before disposal. Autoclave all cultures and contaminated glassware at 15 pounds pressure per square inch (103.4 Pa) for 20 minutes. Disposable plates should be incinerated.

SAFETY PROCEDURES WITH MICROSCOPES

Never use direct sunlight as a light source for the microscope. The lenses may concentrate the light and cause permanent retinal damage. With a soft cloth dipped in isopropyl alcohol, clean the eyepiece of each microscope between viewers. Make sure any electrical cords are out of the main traffic pattern of the classroom.

SAFETY PROCEDURES WITH DISSECTIONS

Handle sharp and pointed instruments with care. Make sure the specimen is firmly secured on a dissection tray or cutting board. Caution students never to dissect a hand-held specimen. Make sure that the scalpels and scissors are sharp and adequate for the job. If razor blades are used for cutting tissues for slide mounts, use only single-edge noninjectable blades. Dissecting instruments should not be removed from the laboratory and should be stored in a locked cabinet.

Formaldehyde has been identified as a carcinogen and mutagen. Any formaldehyde-preserved specimens in the stockroom or classroom should be removed from the school site by qualified health authorities or a licensed commercial company. Specimens are now sold in alternative preservatives. Follow the instructions on the package for preparing specimens for dissection. Most should be rinsed in running water before use. Some may need to be soaked in water overnight if the preservative is particularly strong smelling. Specimens that have not been preserved should be used sparingly and only for a short time. Use only healthy specimens. Instruct students to wear masks and gloves to guard against infection. After dissection, specimens should be discarded in separate containers that can be transported to an incineration site.

FIELD STUDIES

Before taking the students on a field study, examine the area for possible safety hazards. Look for terrain or water hazards and poisonous plants and animals. Obtain the necessary written permission from parents and school authorities. Instruct students on proper dress and behavior. Make sure that students are thoroughly familiar with the investigations they are to conduct. If students are to form small groups, decide in advance when and where they will reassemble. Do not allow any student to travel alone.

Identify any students who have special health problems, especially allergies. Alert these students to potential hazards. Be sure they are adequately prepared to deal with emergencies.

Guidelines for the Use and Care of Animals

Animals are an essential part of a science curriculum. Few things are as interesting and motivating to students as animals. The judicious use of live or preserved animals can help students realize that the study of science is relevant, fascinating, rewarding, and not merely another dull textbook exercise.

Although there are many advantages to providing students with opportunities to study real animals, it is important to be aware of, and sensitive to, ethical and practical concerns. The purpose of this section is to discuss some realistic guidelines for using animals in the classroom. The final decision regarding the use of animals in your classroom should take into consideration these recommendations, local and school guidelines, your personal views, and your assessment of your students' needs, interests, maturity, and ability to behave responsibly.

1. Whenever possible, live animals should be observed in their natural habitats or in zoos, parks, and aquaria.
2. Check the state and federal codes regarding animal welfare that apply in your area. You may also wish to refer to guidelines published by the National Science Teachers' Association, the National Association of Biology Teachers, and the International Science Fair. Make students aware of all safety rules and regulations regarding animals.
3. Before bringing a live animal into the classroom, determine whether a proper habitat can be maintained in the classroom situation. Such a habitat includes temperature, space, and type of food. Students should have a clear understanding of the appropriate care needed by the live animals brought into the classroom. Do not allow students to tap on animal enclosures or otherwise disturb the animals.
4. No wild vertebrate animals should be brought into the classroom. Purchase animals from a reputable dealer only.
5. Live animals should be nonpoisonous and healthy. Any mammals used in the classroom should be vaccinated against rabies unless the animals were purchased recently from a reliable scientific supply company. Quarantine any animal to make sure it is disease-free before bringing it into the classroom.
6. Make sure that the living quarters of classroom animals are clean, located away from stressful situations, appropriately spacious, and secure enough to confine the animal. You may wish to lock cages to prevent the accidental release of animals; the small padlocks used on luggage are good for this purpose.
7. Remove wastes from animal living quarters daily. Thoroughly clean animal living quarters periodically to ensure that they are odor- and germ-free. Provide a daily supply of fresh water and any other need specific to the particular animal.
8. Provide for the care of animals during weekends and school vacations. Inform the custodial staff of the presence of animals and warn them of any special requirements. For example, turning off the aquarium pump to save electricity or spraying the classroom for insects can be fatal to animal collections.
9. Students should be instructed as to how to handle each species brought into the classroom. For example, students can receive painful wounds from the improper handling of some fishes, mollusks, and sea urchins.
10. Animals should be handled only if necessary. If an animal is frightened or excited, pregnant, feeding, or with its young, special handling is required.
11. Students should thoroughly clean their hands after handling animals or the cage containing animals.
12. Animals should be returned to their natural habitat after an observation period of not longer than 14 days. However, laboratory-bred animals or species that are not indigenous to an area should not be released into the environment.
13. If an animal must be euthanized, do not allow students to watch. Do the sacrificing humanely. Contact the local humane society for advice.
14. Before performing any experiment involving live animals, check local and state regulations. In some states, certification is required before a teacher is permitted to experiment with animals.
15. No animal studies involving anesthetic drugs, pathogenic organisms, toxicological products, carcinogens, or radiation should be performed.
16. Any experiment requiring live animals should have a clearly defined objective relating to the teaching/learning of some scientific principle.

17. No experimental procedures that will cause pain, discomfort, or harm to mammals, birds, reptiles, fishes, and amphibians should be done in the classroom or at home.
18. Surgical procedures should not be performed on live vertebrate animals.
19. If fertilized bird eggs are opened, the embryo should be destroyed humanely two days before it would have hatched, at the latest.
20. Whenever possible, substitute plants or invertebrate animals for vertebrates.
21. When working with preserved animals, make sure that students maintain a serious and respectful attitude toward the specimens.

HANDLING ETHICAL ISSUES

There is much controversy regarding the use of animals in scientific research. This controversy extends to preserved animals in dissections as well as to live animals in experiments. Although the battle over what uses of animals are appropriate in a science classroom can be frustrating and emotionally charged, it can also provide an opportunity for students to closely examine a current issue. You may wish to have students read current literature on the subject and contact groups and individuals with varying points of view.

Stress that it is important to make a rational, informed decision before taking a stand on any issue. Point out that it is vital to know and understand the arguments on both sides of an issue. Help students analyze the sources they find in terms of slant, bias, and the reliability and objectivity of the author(s). Teach them to learn to distinguish between fact and opinion. Encourage them to question what they read and hear. Challenge them to discover the hidden assumptions and implications of different points of view.

If dissections are a part of your curriculum and a student chooses to avoid dissections because of ethical concerns, you should respect that student's opinion. Point out, however, that no simulation or videotape can replace hands-on, firsthand experience.

NABT GUIDELINES FOR THE USE OF LIVE ANIMALS

> **The National Association of Biology Teachers (NABT) has developed the following set of guidelines to be used when working with live animals.**

Living things are the subject of science, and their direct study is an appropriate and necessary part of science teaching. Textbook instruction alone cannot provide students with a basic understanding of life and life processes. We further recognize the importance of research to understanding life processes and providing information on health, disease, medical care, and agriculture.

The abuse of any living organism for experimentation or any other purpose is intolerable in any segment of society. Because science deals specifically with living things, professional educators must be especially cognizant of their responsibility to prevent inhumane treatment to living organisms in the name of science and research. This responsibility should extend beyond the confines of the teacher's classroom to the rest of the school and community.

The National Association of Biology Teachers, in speaking to the dilemma of providing a sound science education while addressing the problem of humane experimentation, presents the following guidelines on the use of live animals.

A. Science experimentation should lead to and be consistent with a respect for life and all living things. Humane treatment and care of animals should be an integral part of any lesson that includes living animals.
B. All aspects of exercises and/or experiments dealing with living things must be within the comprehension and capabilities of the students involved. It is recognized that these parameters are necessarily vague, but it is expected that competent teachers of science recognize these limitations.
C. Lower orders of life, such as bacteria, fungi, protozoans, and invertebrates, can reveal much basic science information and are preferable as subjects for invasive studies wherever and whenever possible.
D. Vertebrate animals may be used as experimental organisms in the following situations:
  1. Observations of normal living patterns of wild animals in the free-living state or in zoological parks, gardens, or aquaria.
  2. Observations of normal living patterns of pets, fish, or domestic animals.
  3. Observations of science phenomena, i.e., including ovulation in frogs through hormone injections that do not cause discomfort or adverse effects to the animals.
E. Animals should be properly cared for as described in the following guidelines:
  1. Appropriate quarters for the animals being used should be provided in a place free

© Prentice-Hall, Inc.

from undue stresses. If housed in the classroom itself, animals should not be constantly subjected to disturbances that might be caused by students in the classroom or other upsetting activities.

2. All animals used in teaching or research programs must receive proper care. Quarters should provide for sanitation, protection from the elements, and have sufficient space for normal behavioral and postural requirements of the species. Quarters shall be easily cleaned, ventilated, and lighted. Proper temperature regulation shall be provided.

3. Proper food and clean drinking water for those animals requiring water shall be available at all times in suitable containers.

4. Animals' care shall be supervised by a science teacher experienced in proper animal care.

5. If euthanasia is necessary, animals shall be sacrificed in an approved, humane manner by an adult experienced in the use of such procedures. Laboratory animals should not be released in the environment if they were not originally a part of the native fauna. The introduction of nonnative species, which may become feral, must be avoided.

6. The procurement and use of wild or domestic animals must comply with existing local, state, or federal rules regarding same.

F. Animal studies should be carried out under the provisions of the following guidelines:

1. All animal studies should be carried out under the direct supervision of a competent science teacher. It is the responsibility of that teacher to ensure that the student has the necessary comprehension of the study being done.

2. Students should not be allowed to take animals home to carry out experimental studies. These studies should be done in a suitable area in the school.

3. Students doing projects with vertebrate animals should adhere to the following:

a. No experimental procedures should be attempted that would subject vertebrate animals to pain or distinct discomfort, or interfere with their health in any way. Pithing of live frogs should be carried out by a teacher experienced in such procedures and should not be part of the general class activity.

b. Students should not perform surgery on living vertebrate animals except under the direct supervision of a qualified biomedical scientist.

4. Experimental procedures should not involve the use of microorganisms pathogenic to humans or other animals, ionizing radiation, carcinogens, drugs, or chemicals at toxic levels, drugs known to produce adverse or teratogenic effects, pain-causing drugs, alcohol in any form, electric shock, exercise until exhaustion, or other distressing stimuli.

5. Behavioral studies should use only positive reinforcement in training studies.

6. Egg embryos subjected to experimental manipulation must be destroyed humanely at least two days prior to hatching. Normal egg embryos allowed to hatch must be treated humanely within these guidelines.

7. The administration of anesthetics should be carried out by a qualified science teacher competent in such procedures. (The legal ramifications of student use of anesthetics are complex, and such use should be avoided.)

G. The use of living animals for science fair projects and displays shall be in accordance with these guidelines. In addition, no living vertebrate animals shall be used in displays for science fair exhibitions.

H. It is recognized that an exceptionally talented student may wish to conduct original research in the biological or medical sciences. In those cases where the research value of a specific project is obvious by its potential contribution to science, but its execution would be otherwise prohibited by the guidelines governing the selection of an appropriate experimental animal or procedure, exceptions can be obtained if:

1. the project is approved by and carried out under the direct supervision of a qualified biomedical scientist or a designated adult supervisor in the field of the investigation; and

2. the project is carried out in an appropriate research facility; and

3. the project is carried out with the utmost regard for the humane care and treatment of the animals involved in the project; and

4. a research plan is developed and approved by the qualified biomedical scientist prior to the start of any research.

Laboratory Materials and Equipment

Note: Safety equipment has not been listed. It is recommended that a laboratory apron, safety goggles, and heat-resistant gloves be worn when required.

Item	Quantity per Group	Laboratory Investigation
Aluminum foil	1 roll	2
Ball, Styrofoam	1	4
Bunsen burner	1	1
Burette	1	6
Burette clamp	1	6
	2	7
Calcium chloride	1 bottle	1
Card, 20 cm × 25 cm	1	2
10 cm × 15 cm	1	2
Cardboard	1 piece	3
Dowel, 30 cm long	1	7
Drawing compass	1	2
Fishing line, nylon	75 cm	4
Fishing sinker, 113 g or more	1	7
Lamp, incandescent	1	8
Masking tape	1 roll	4, 8
Meterstick	1	2, 5, 6
Metric ruler	1	3, 4, 9
Nichrome wire test loops	4	1
Paper	1 sheet	3
	2 sheets	5
lined	1 sheet	7
Paper clip	1	4
Pencil	1	3
colored	assorted	1, 9
Pie plate	1	6
Potassium chloride	1 bottle	1
Razor blade, single-edged	1	2
Ring stand	1	6
	2	7
Scissors	1	2, 4, 5, 7
Sodium chloride	1 bottle	1
Spectroscope	1	1
String	15 cm	3
	1.5 m	6
Strontium chloride	1 bottle	1
Tape	1 roll	2, 5
Thermometers, Celsius	3	8
Thread	1 roll	7
Thumbtacks	2	3
Tubing, glass	15 cm	4
Washers, metal	25	4
Watch or clock	1	6, 8
Weight, 500 g	1	6
Wooden blocks (see Lab)	3	8

© Prentice-Hall, Inc.

Suppliers of Laboratory Materials and Equipment

Accent Science
P.O. Box 1444
Saginaw, MI 48605

Analytical Scientific
11049 Bandera Road
San Antonio, TX 78250

Andor Chemical Corporation
P.O. Box K
Rochester, NY 14623

Ann Arbor Biologicals
6780 Jackson Road
Ann Arbor, MI 48103

Apple Computer, Inc.
20525 Mariani Avenue
Cupertino, CA 95014

Aquarium and Science Supply
   Company
P.O. Box 41
Dresher, PA 19025

Arbor Scientific
P.O. Box 2750
924 North Main Street
Ann Arbor, MI 48106

Bausch & Lomb
Scientific Optical Products Division
P.O. Box 450
1400 North Goodman Street
Rochester, NY 14692-0450

California Corporation of
   Biochemical Research
3625 Medford Street
Los Angeles, CA 90063

Carolina Biological Supply Company
2700 York Road
Burlington, NC 27215

Central Scientific Company
   (CENCO)
11222 Melrose Avenue
Franklin Park, IL 60131

Chem Scientific, Inc.
67 Chapel Street
Newton, MA 02158

College Biological Supply Company
8857 Mount Israel Road
Escondido, CA 92025

Connecticut Valley Biological
   Supply Company, Inc.
P.O. Box 326
82 Valley Road
Southampton, MA 01073

Damon/Instructional Systems
   Division
80 Wilson Way
Westwood, MA 02090

Delta Biologicals
P.O. Box 26666
Tucson, AZ 85726-6666

Edmund Scientific Company
101 East Gloucester Pike
Barrington, NJ 08007-1380

Fisher Scientific Company
Educational Materials Division
4901 West LeMoyne Street
Chicago, IL 60651

Flinn Scientific, Inc.
P.O. Box 219
131 Flinn Street
Batavia, IL 60510

Forestry Suppliers, Inc.
P.O. Box 8397
205 West Rankin Street
Jackson, MS 39204

Frey Scientific Company
905 Hickory Lane
Mansfield, OH 44905

General Supply Corporation
P.O. Box 9347
Jackson, MS 39206

Grau-Hall Scientific Corporation
6501 Elvas Avenue
Sacramento, CA 95819

H & H Research, Inc.
P.O. Box 5156, Station One
Wilmington, NC 28403

Hach Company
P.O. Box 389
Loveland, CO 80539

Harvard Apparatus Company
Dover, MA 02118

Hubbard Scientific Company
P.O. Box 104
1946 Raymond Drive
Northbrook, IL 60062

Ideal School Supply Company
11000 South Lavergne Avenue
Oak Lawn, IL 60453

Kons Scientific Company, Inc.
P.O. Box 3
Germantown, WI 53022-0003

La Pine Scientific Company
6001 Knox Avenue
Chicago, IL 60018

Lab-Aids, Inc.
249 Trade Zone Drive
Ronkonkoma, NY 11779

Learning Alternatives
P.O. Box 219
Vienna, OH 44473

Learning Spectrum
1390 Westridge Drive
Portola Valley, CA 94025

Learning Things, Inc.
P.O. Box 436
68A Broadway
Arlington, MA 02174

William A. Lemberger Company
2500 Waukau Avenue
Oshkosh, WI 54903

McKilligan Supply Corporation
435 Main Street
Johnson City, NY 13790

Ben Meadows Company
3589 Broad Street
Chamblee, GA 30341

Merrell Scientific Division
Educational Modules,
  Incorporated
1665 Buffalo Road
Rochester, NY 14624

Nasco
901 Janesville Avenue
Fort Atkinson, WI 53538

Nasco West, Inc.
P.O. Box 3837
Modesto, CA 95352

National Teaching Aids, Inc.
1845 Highland Avenue
New Hyde Park, NY 11040

Niles Biological
P.O. Box 191543
Sacramento, CA 95819

Norris Science Labs & Kits
P.O. Box 61281
Las Vegas, NV 89160

Nutritional Biochemicals
  Corporation
26201 Miles Road
Cleveland, OH 44128

Parco Scientific Company
P.O. Box 189
316 Youngstown-Kingsville Road
Vienna, OH 44473

Phipps and Bird, Inc.
P.O. Box 189
Richmond, VA 23261

Prentice-Hall Equipment Division
10 Oriskany Drive
Tonawanda, NY 14150

Redco Science, Inc.
11 Robinson Lane
Oxford, CT 06483

Sargent-Welch Scientific Company
7300 North Linder Avenue
Skokie, IL 60077

Scavengers Scientific Supply
  Company
P.O. Box 211328
Auke Bay, WI 99821

Schoolmasters Science
P.O. Box 1941
745 State Circle
Ann Arbor, MI 48106

Schwarz BioResearch, Inc.
Mountain View Avenue
Orangeburg, NY 10962

Science Kit and Boreal Labs
777 East Park Drive
Tonawanda, NY 14150

The Science Man Company
A Division of TSM Marketing, Inc.
4738 North Harlem Avenue
Harwood Heights, IL 60656

Scientific Glass Apparatus
  Company
737 Broad Street
Bloomfield, NJ 07003

Southern Precision Instrument
  Company
3419 East Commerce Street
San Antonio, TX 78820

Southwestern Biological Supply
  Company
P.O. Box 4084
Dallas, TX 75208

Spectrum Educational Supplies
  Limited
125 Mary Street
Aurora, Ontario, Canada

Swift Instruments, Inc.
P.O. Box 562
San Jose, CA 95106

Triarch, Inc.
P.O. Box 98
Ripon, WI 59471

Turtox, Inc.
P.O. Box 266
Palos Heights, IL 60463-0266

Ward's Natural Science
  Establishment, Inc.
P.O. Box 92912
5100 West Henrietta Road
Rochester, NY 14692-9012

Wildlife Supply Company
301 Cass Street
Saginaw, MI 48602

Wilkens-Anderson Company
4525 West Division Street
Chicago, IL 60651

© Prentice-Hall, Inc.

Laboratory Manual

EXPLORING THE UNIVERSE

Prentice Hall
Englewood Cliffs, New Jersey
Needham, Massachusetts

Laboratory Manual

PRENTICE HALL SCIENCE
Exploring the Universe

© 1993 by Prentice-Hall, Inc., Englewood Cliffs, New Jersey 07632.
All rights reserved. Printed in the United States of America.

ISBN 0-13-985821-0

   13 14 15   99 98 97 96

Prentice Hall
A Division of Simon & Schuster
Englewood Cliffs, New Jersey 07632

Contents

Safety Symbols

All the investigations in this *Laboratory Manual* have been designed with safety in mind. If you follow the instructions, you should have a safe and interesting year in the laboratory. Before beginning any investigation, make sure you read the safety rules that follow.

The eight safety symbols below appear next to certain steps in some of the investigations in this *Laboratory Manual*. The symbols alert you to the need for special safety precautions. The description of each symbol below tells you which precautions to take whenever you see the symbol in an investigation.

Glassware Safety
1. Whenever you see this symbol, you will know that you are working with glassware that can easily be broken. Take particular care to handle such glassware safely. And never use broken or chipped glassware.
2. Never heat glassware that is not thoroughly dry. Never pick up any glassware unless you are sure it is not hot. If it is hot, use heat-resistant gloves.
3. Always clean glassware thoroughly before putting it away.

Fire Safety
1. Whenever you see this symbol, you will know that you are working with fire. Never use any source of fire without wearing safety goggles.
2. Never heat anything—particularly chemicals—unless instructed to do so.
3. Never heat anything in a closed container.
4. Never reach across a flame.
5. Always use a clamp, tongs, or heat-resistant gloves to handle hot objects.
6. Always maintain a clean work area, particularly when using a flame.

Heat Safety
Whenever you see this symbol, you will know that you should put on heat-resistant gloves to avoid burning your hands.

Chemical Safety
1. Whenever you see this symbol, you will know that you are working with chemicals that could be hazardous.
2. Never smell any chemical directly from its container. Always use your hand to waft some of the odors from the top of the container toward your nose—and only when instructed to do so.
3. Never mix chemicals unless instructed to do so.
4. Never touch or taste any chemical unless instructed to do so.
5. Keep all lids closed when chemicals are not in use. Dispose of all chemicals as instructed by your teacher.
6. Immediately rinse with water any chemicals, particularly acids, that get on your skin and clothes. Then notify your teacher.

Eye and Face Safety
1. Whenever you see this symbol, you will know that you are performing an experiment in which you must take precautions to protect your eyes and face by wearing safety goggles.
2. When you are heating a test tube or bottle, always point it away from you and others. Chemicals can splash or boil out of a heated test tube.

Sharp Instrument Safety
1. Whenever you see this symbol, you will know that you are working with a sharp instrument.
2. Always use single-edged razors; double-edged razors are too dangerous.
3. Handle any sharp instrument with extreme care. Never cut any material toward you; always cut away from you.
4. Immediately notify your teacher if your skin is cut.

Electrical Safety
1. Whenever you see this symbol, you will know that you are using electricity in the laboratory.
2. Never use long extension cords to plug in any electrical device. Do not plug too many appliances into one socket or you may overload the socket and cause a fire.
3. Never touch an electrical appliance or outlet with wet hands.

Animal Safety
1. Whenever you see this symbol, you will know that you are working with live animals.
2. Do not cause pain, discomfort, or injury to an animal.
3. Follow your teacher's directions when handling animals. Wash your hands thoroughly after handling animals or their cages.

Science Safety Rules

One of the first things a scientist learns is that working in the laboratory can be an exciting experience. But the laboratory can also be quite dangerous if proper safety rules are not followed at all times. To prepare yourself for a safe year in the laboratory, read over the following safety rules. Then read them a second time. Make sure you understand each rule. If you do not, ask your teacher to explain any rules you are unsure of.

Dress Code

1. Many materials in the laboratory can cause eye injury. To protect yourself from possible injury, wear safety goggles whenever you are working with chemicals, burners, or any substance that might get into your eyes. Never wear contact lenses in the laboratory.

2. Wear a laboratory apron or coat whenever you are working with chemicals or heated substances.

3. Tie back long hair to keep it away from any chemicals, burners, and candles, or other laboratory equipment.

4. Remove or tie back any article of clothing or jewelry that can hang down and touch chemicals and flames.

General Safety Rules

5. Read all directions for an experiment several times. Follow the directions exactly as they are written. If you are in doubt about any part of the experiment, ask your teacher for assistance.

6. Never perform activities that are not authorized by your teacher. Obtain permission before "experimenting" on your own.

7. Never handle any equipment unless you have specific permission.

8. Take extreme care not to spill any material in the laboratory. If a spill occurs, immediately ask your teacher about the proper cleanup procedure. Never simply pour chemicals or other substances into the sink or trash container.

9. Never eat in the laboratory.

10. Wash your hands before and after each experiment.

First Aid

11. Immediately report all accidents, no matter how minor, to your teacher.

12. Learn what to do in case of specific accidents, such as getting acid in your eyes or on your skin. (Rinse acids from your body with lots of water.)

13. Become aware of the location of the first-aid kit. But your teacher should administer any required first aid due to injury. Or your teacher may send you to the school nurse or call a physician.

14. Know where and how to report an accident or fire. Find out the location of the fire extinguisher, phone, and fire alarm. Keep a list of important phone numbers—such as the fire department and the school nurse—near the phone. Immediately report any fires to your teacher.

Heating and Fire Safety

15. Again, never use a heat source, such as a candle or a burner, without wearing safety goggles.

16. Never heat a chemical you are not instructed to heat. A chemical that is harmless when cool may be dangerous when heated.

17. Maintain a clean work area and keep all materials away from flames.

18. Never reach across a flame.

19. Make sure you know how to light a Bunsen burner. (Your teacher will demonstrate the proper procedure for lighting a burner.) If the flame leaps out of a burner toward you, immediately turn off the gas. Do not touch the burner. It may be hot. And never leave a lighted burner unattended!

20. When heating a test tube or bottle, always point it away from you and others. Chemicals can splash or boil out of a heated test tube.

21. Never heat a liquid in a closed container. The expanding gases produced may blow the container apart, injuring you or others.
22. Before picking up a container that has been heated, first hold the back of your hand near it. If you can feel the heat on the back of your hand, the container may be too hot to handle. Use a clamp or tongs when handling hot containers.

Using Chemicals Safely

23. Never mix chemicals for the "fun of it." You might produce a dangerous, possibly explosive substance.
24. Never touch, taste, or smell a chemical unless you are instructed by your teacher to do so. Many chemicals are poisonous. If you are instructed to note the fumes in an experiment, gently wave your hand over the opening of a container and direct the fumes toward your nose. Do not inhale the fumes directly from the container.
25. Use only those chemicals needed in the activity. Keep all lids closed when a chemical is not being used. Notify your teacher whenever chemicals are spilled.
26. Dispose of all chemicals as instructed by your teacher. To avoid contamination, never return chemicals to their original containers.
27. Be extra careful when working with acids or bases. Pour such chemicals over the sink, not over your workbench.
28. When diluting an acid, pour the acid into water. Never pour water into the acid.
29. Immediately rinse with water any acids that get on your skin or clothing. Then notify your teacher of any acid spill.

Using Glassware Safely

30. Never force glass tubing into a rubber stopper. A turning motion and lubricant will be helpful when inserting glass tubing into rubber stoppers or rubber tubing. Your teacher will demonstrate the proper way to insert glass tubing.
31. Never heat glassware that is not thoroughly dry. Use a wire screen to protect glassware from any flame.
32. Keep in mind that hot glassware will not appear hot. Never pick up glassware without first checking to see if it is hot. See #22.
33. If you are instructed to cut glass tubing, fire-polish the ends immediately to remove sharp edges.
34. Never use broken or chipped glassware. If glassware breaks, notify your teacher and dispose of the glassware in the proper trash container.
35. Never eat or drink from laboratory glassware.
36. Thoroughly clean glassware before putting it away.

Using Sharp Instruments

37. Handle scalpels or razor blades with extreme care. Never cut material toward you; cut away from you.
38. Immediately notify your teacher if you cut your skin when working in the laboratory.

Animal Safety

39. No experiments that cause pain, discomfort, or harm to mammals, birds, reptiles, fish, and amphibians should be done in the classroom or at home.
40. Animals should be handled only if necessary. If an animal is excited or frightened, pregnant, feeding, or with its young, special handling is required.
41. Your teacher will instruct you as to how to handle each animal species that may be brought into the classroom.
42. Clean your hands thoroughly after handling animals or the cage containing animals.

End-of-Experiment Rules

43. After an experiment has been completed, clean up your work area and return all equipment to its proper place.
44. Wash your hands after every experiment.
45. Turn off all candles and burners before leaving the laboratory. Check that the gas line leading to the burner is off as well.

Name _____ Class _____ Date _____

_____ *Laboratory Investigation* _____

Comparing Chemical Composition and the Spectrum

You may want to refer students to pages M22–M25 in their textbook for a general discussion of spectral analysis of stars.

Time required: 40 minutes

Background Information

Scientists can learn about stars and other bodies in space by studying the spectrum, or component colors, of the light these objects give off. When substances are heated, they give off light of different colors. A spectroscope is a device that breaks light into its component colors. By using a spectroscope to examine the light an object gives off, the chemical composition of the substance can be determined.

In this investigation you will use a spectroscope to examine the spectra of several different substances and then determine the chemical composition of an unknown sample.

Problem

How can astronomers learn about distant stars?

Materials (per group)

hand-held spectroscope
4 nichrome wire test loops
samples of calcium chloride,   Chemicals may be ordered from any science supply company.
    strontium chloride, potassium
    chloride, and sodium chloride
Bunsen burner or alcohol
    burner
safety goggles
colored pencils

Procedure

🔥 1. Light and adjust the burner to give a hot, blue flame.

🔥 2. Look at the flame through the spectroscope. The slit of the spectroscope should be vertical. The eyepiece should be rotated to provide a sharp spectrum on the side wall of the spectroscope.

🔥 3. While you are looking at the flame through the spectroscope, have one of your groupmates carefully dip the nichrome wire into the sample of calcium chloride and place the sample in the flame. In the space below, draw what you see through the spectroscope as the sample glows. Use colored pencils or label the colors that you see. Trade places with your groupmates and allow each group member to observe the spectrum of calcium chloride.

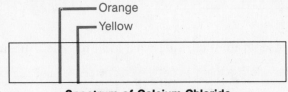

Spectrum of Calcium Chloride
Bands will appear orange and yellow.

© Prentice-Hall, Inc.   **Exploring the Universe   M ■ 7**

4. Repeat step 3 with the samples of sodium chloride, potassium chloride, and strontium chloride. **Note:** *Be sure to use a separate nichrome wire loop for each substance.* Draw the spectrum for each substance in the spaces provided below.

Spectrum of Sodium Chloride
Strong yellow band will be seen.

Spectrum of Potassium Chloride
Bands will appear in the violet end.

Spectrum of Strontium Chloride
Bands will be seen in the red end.

5. When you have finished, obtain a sample of the unknown substance from your teacher. Repeat step 3. Observe and record the spectrum of the unknown sample in the space below.

Spectrum of Unknown

Observations

1. How did the spectra of the samples differ?

By the brightness, location, and color of the lines.

2. If all the bands you observed were drawn on one band, what would it look like?

The spectrum of visible light from red at one end to violet at the other.

Analysis and Conclusions

1. What might the unknown sample contain? How do you know?

Answers will vary depending on the unknown used. The unknown can be identified by comparing its

spectrum with the spectrum of the samples.

2. How can scientists tell what substances may be in a distant star?

By examining its spectrum and comparing it to known spectra.

3. Why must you use a separate nichrome wire loop for each substance?

You must avoid contamination so that you get the characteristic spectrum of the particular compound,

and no other compound.

Critical Thinking and Application

1. How do the samples resemble stars? The stars and the samples emit light. _____

   _____

2. What other device besides a spectroscope breaks light into its component colors?

   A prism. _____

3. Spectral lines are often called the "fingerprints" of the elements. Why do you think this

   is so? Each element has its own unique set of spectral lines. _____

   _____

   _____

4. Why do you think these compounds give off light having a characteristic spectrum when

   they are heated? The compounds gain energy from the heat. The electrons in the atoms of the

   component elements use this energy to "climb" to a higher energy level. The electrons soon lose this

   energy and fall back to their original position. The specific amount of energy corresponds to a particular

   spectrum. _____

   _____

Going Further

1. Observe the spectra of light from 25-watt, 40-watt, 60-watt, and 100-watt light bulbs. How do the spectra differ? How can scientists determine the temperature of a distant star by using a spectroscope?

2. Have you ever noticed how a train whistle or ambulance siren sounds different when it is coming toward you than when it is going away from you? The spectrum of light looks different when the light source is coming toward you or going away from you. This is known as the Doppler effect. Using one of the light bulbs, have your partner move it toward you as you observe it through the spectroscope. Then have your partner move it away from you. What changes do you notice? How can scientists determine if a distant star is coming toward the Earth or going away from it?

© Prentice-Hall, Inc.

Laboratory Investigation

2

Measuring the Diameter of the Sun

You may want to refer students to pages M28–M30 in their textbook for a general discussion of the size of the sun.

Time required: 40 minutes

Background Information

Even though the Earth is nearly 150,000,000 km from the sun at its closest approach, it is still possible to make accurate measurements of the sun's size by using instruments. In this investigation you will construct a simple device and use it to collect data that will allow you to calculate the diameter of the sun.

Problem

What is the diameter of the sun and how can it be determined?

Materials (per group)

meterstick
card, 20 cm × 25 cm
card, 10 cm × 15 cm
scissors
tape
small square piece of aluminum
    foil
drawing compass or pin
single-edged razor blade

Procedure

1. Use the razor blade to carefully cut slits in each card in the positions shown in Figure 1 so that the meterstick can fit through them. Cut each slit in the form of a capital "I." Make the openings small enough so that the meterstick fits tightly.

2. Draw two parallel lines exactly 0.8 cm apart near the center of the small card as shown in Figure 1.

3. Cut a large square hole in the larger card and cover it with aluminum foil. Use tape to hold the foil securely in place. Punch a very small hole near the center of the foil with a compass point or a pin.

4. Place the large card near one end of the meterstick and tape it in place. Be careful to fasten it so that it is perpendicular to the meterstick. Place the small card on the other end. For best results, the cards must be kept perpendicular to the meterstick.

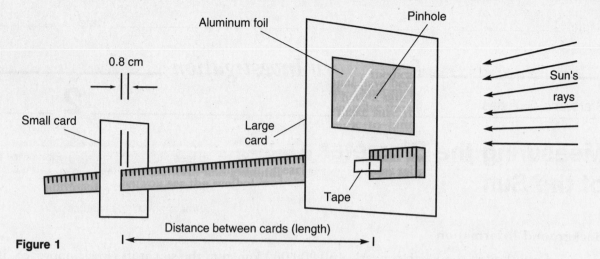

Figure 1

5. Aim the end of the meterstick that has the foil-covered card on it toward the sun. **CAUTION:** *Do not look at the sun; you may damage your eyes.* Move the meterstick around until the shadow of the large card covers the smaller card. A bright image of the sun will fall on the smaller card. Move the smaller card until the bright image of the sun exactly fills the space between the two parallel lines on the smaller card.

6. Be certain both cards are perpendicular to the meterstick. Then determine the distance between the two cards. Measure the distance to the nearest 0.1 cm and record it in the Data Table. Also record the diameter of the image.

Observations

DATA TABLE

Distance Between Two Cards	Diameter of Sun's Image
Answers will vary.	0.8 cm

Analysis and Conclusions

1. Using the formula below, calculate the diameter of the sun.

$$\frac{\text{diameter of the sun (km)}}{\text{distance to the sun (km)}} = \frac{\text{diameter of the sun's image (cm)}}{\text{distance between two cards (cm)}}$$

Note: *The diameter of the sun's image is 0.8 cm, since it equals the width of the small card's slit.* The average distance between the Earth and sun is approximately 150,000,000 km.

Answers will vary but should be approximately 1,391,000 km.

2. The actual diameter of the sun is 1,391,000 km. Using the formula below, determine the amount of error in your calculated value for the sun's diameter.

$$\text{Percentage of error} = \frac{\text{difference between your value and the correct value}}{\text{correct value}} \times 100$$

Answers will vary.

3. What could account for your error in calculating the sun's diameter?

The students used an average value for the distance between the sun and the Earth; in fact, the distance varies from a maximum of 152,086,000 km to a minimum of 147,097,000 km.

Critical Thinking and Application

1. How might the technique used in this investigation be useful in making other astronomical measurements? If the light is bright enough, the diameter of the moon could be measured. With a light-gathering instrument such as a telescope, the diameters of stars and planets could be measured.

2. How is the technique used in this investigation related to the construction of a camera?

In a camera, light comes through a tiny opening and an image forms on the film inside the camera.

3. How might clouds in the sky affect the accuracy of your measurement in this investigation? If a cloud partially covers the sun, the image might appear smaller in diameter than it normally would. Total cloud cover would probably make the image too faint to be seen and measured properly.

© Prentice-Hall, Inc.

Going Further

Using the value you obtained for the sun's diameter and the formula below, calculate the circumference of the sun. The value of π (pi) is approximately 3.14.

$$\text{Circumference} = \pi \times \text{diameter}$$

Using the actual diameter of the sun, which is given above, calculate the actual circumference of the sun.

Using the two values for the sun's circumference, calculate the percentage of error for the value you obtained from your experimental data.

Name _____ Class _____ Date _____

Laboratory Investigation

3

Characteristics of Elliptical Orbits

You may want to refer students to pages M61–M62 in their textbook for a general discussion of elliptical orbits.

Time required: 40 minutes

Background Information

The shape of the school track is called an ellipse. The shape of the orbit of each planet in our solar system is also an ellipse. Unlike a circle, which is a curved shape drawn around a single point, an ellipse is a curved shape that is drawn around two points. Each of these points is called a focus; together they are called the foci of the ellipse. An ellipse is described as eccentric because it is not shaped like a circle. The more unlike a circle an ellipse becomes, the more eccentric the ellipse is said to be.

In this investigation you will draw an ellipse, calculate its eccentricity, and predict the shape of the Earth's orbit.

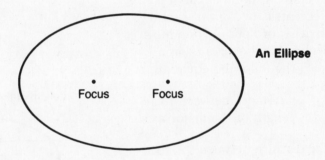

An Ellipse

Focus   Focus

Problem

What is the shape of the Earth's orbit?

Materials (*per group*)

pencil
sheet of paper
2 thumbtacks
piece of string approximately
    15 cm long
piece of cardboard at least as
    large as the sheet of paper
metric ruler

Corrugated cardboard works well, but any surface will do as long as it easily accepts tacks.

Procedure

1. Tie the ends of the string together to form a loop. The loop should be about 55 mm long when stretched tight, but it can safely vary by up to 5 mm either way.

© Prentice-Hall, Inc.

2. Fold a sheet of paper into thirds; then flatten it out. This will help you to properly space the ellipses that you are about to draw.

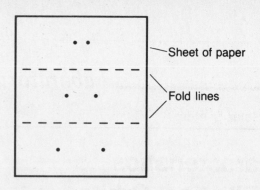

Figure 1

3. In the top third of the paper, make two dots 2 cm apart. In the middle third, make two dots 3 cm apart. In the bottom third, make two dots 4 cm apart. See Figure 1.

4. Place the sheet of paper on the piece of cardboard. Carefully push two tacks through one set of points. Place the string loop around the tacks. Then use a pencil to draw an ellipse around the two foci, pulling the string tight against the tacks. See Figure 2. Using the same procedure, draw an ellipse around each of the two remaining sets of points.   Have students push the tacks in far enough to be secure but leave enough room for the string loop to move freely.

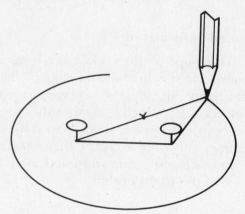

Figure 2

5. Because an ellipse is not a circle, it is said to be eccentric, or "out of round." The eccentricity, or "out-of-roundness," can be calculated and expressed as a number using the following equation:

$$\text{Eccentricity} = \frac{\text{distance between foci}}{\text{length of the major axis}}$$

Measure the distance between the foci and the length of the major axis for each of the three ellipses you have just drawn. Using the equation above, calculate their eccentricities. Enter your data in the Data Table.

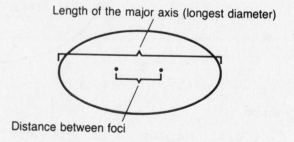

Figure 3

Observations

DATA TABLE

Ellipse	Distance Between Foci (mm)	Length of Major Axis (mm)	Eccentricity
Top (first)	two	Lengths will vary due to differences in loop lengths among students	Eccentricities will vary but they will all fall between a maximum of one and a minimum of zero
Middle (second)	three		
Bottom (third)	four		

Analysis and Conclusions

1. If you were drawing an ellipse, what would happen to its shape if you used the same size

loop but moved the foci farther apart? The shape of the ellipse would become more eccentric (less

like a circle) as the foci were moved farther apart.

_____

2. The eccentricity of an ellipse can be expressed as a number. Does the eccentricity of an ellipse increase, decrease, or remain the same if its shape is changed to make it more nearly round? **Note:** *Refer to the eccentricities of the ellipses you drew in this investigation.*

The more nearly round the shape became, the lower the eccentricity would be. The eccentricity of a

circle is 0.

3. What is the relationship between the eccentricity of an ellipse and how nearly round the

ellipse appears to be? As the eccentricity of an ellipse increases, the shape of the ellipse becomes

less round. The maximum eccentricity would occur when the distance between the foci and the major

axis were equal. This would result in a straight line, and the eccentricity would be 1.

_____

Critical Thinking and Application

1. The figure below represents the Earth's orbit drawn to scale. The sun is located at one of the foci; there is nothing at the other. Measure the distance between the two foci and the major axis for the orbit drawn here. Then calculate the eccentricity of the ellipse. Enter your data in the Data Table.

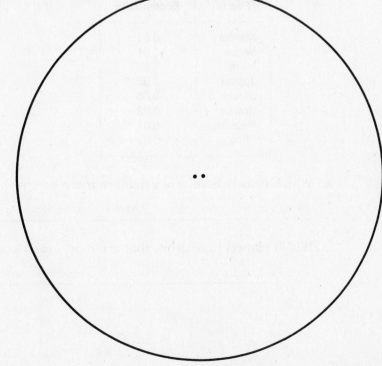

DATA TABLE

Distance between the two foci	= <u>2</u> mm	
Length of major axis	= <u>100</u> mm	
Eccentricity	= <u>0.02</u> mm	

2. Does the Earth's orbit look more or less eccentric than the three ellipses you drew on the sheet of paper? It looks less eccentric. It looks nearly round.

_____

_____

3. Which diagram most accurately shows the shape of the Earth's orbit drawn to scale?

Diagram A.

_____

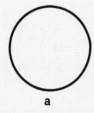
a

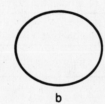
b

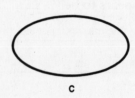
c

Going Further

1. Use the list of planet orbit eccentricities to answer the following questions:

Planet	Eccentricity
Mercury	0.21
Venus	0.01
Mars	0.09
Jupiter	0.05
Saturn	0.06
Uranus	0.05
Neptune	0.01
Pluto	0.25

The Earth's orbit has an eccentricity of 0.02.

a. Which planets have orbits that are more eccentric than the Earth's?

Mercury, Mars, Jupiter, Saturn, Uranus, and Pluto.

_____

b. Which planets have orbits that are most nearly round?

Venus and Neptune. At 0.02, the Earth's orbit looks nearly round.

_____

Laboratory Investigation

4

Relating Gravitational Force and Orbits

You may want to refer students to page M62 in their textbook for a general discussion of the relationship between gravity and orbit.

Time required: 40 minutes

Background Information

Scientists know that the nine planets in the solar system orbit the sun. They also know that the moon orbits the Earth. There is a relationship between the time it takes for a planet to orbit the sun, or its period of revolution, and the gravitational force pulling on the planet. The same relationship is also used to put an artificial satellite in orbit.

In this investigation you will determine the relationship between the period of revolution of an object or body in space and the force pulling on the orbiting object or body.

Problem

What causes planets to orbit the sun or the moon and artificial satellites to orbit the Earth?

Materials *(per group)* Heavy-duty (squash-proof) plastic drinking straw can be substituted for glass tube.

15-cm glass tube, fire polished and taped
scissors
masking tape
75 cm of nylon fishing line

Styrofoam ball, with 10-cm diameter
paper clip
25 small metal washers
metric ruler

Procedure

🝆 1. Thread a 50-cm length of nylon fishing line through the glass tube. Attach the Styrofoam ball to one end by taping the line securely. Bend the paper clip for use as a hanger. Tie the other end of the nylon fishing line to the paper clip. Your experiment setup should look like the one in Figure 1.

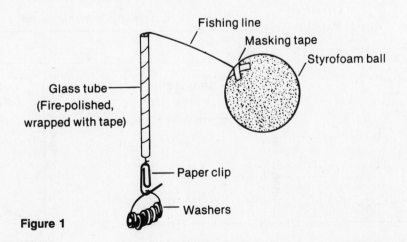

Figure 1

© Prentice-Hall, Inc.

2. Cut a small piece of fishing line about 5 cm long. Loop the string through five washers and tie securely. Hang the loop on the paper clip. See Figure 1. Check the students' setup of equipment before they begin to swing the apparatus.

3. **CAUTION:** *Make sure that no one is near you and there is nothing for the ball to hit.* Using the tube as a handle, carefully whirl the ball around until the paper clip moves up to just below the bottom of the glass tube.

4. When the paper clip moves up just below the bottom of the glass tube, have a group member time ten complete revolutions of the ball. Find the time needed for one revolution by dividing by 10. Record your answer in the Data Table.

5. Repeat steps 2 through 4 with loops of 10, 15, 20, and 25 washers. Record each period of revolution in the Data Table.

Observations

DATA TABLE

Number of Washers	Period of Revolution
5	
10	Answers will vary.
15	
20	
25	

Analysis and Conclusions

1. What does the number of washers represent in this model?

   The gravitational force between the two bodies.

2. What happens to the period of revolution as the gravitational force increases?

   The period of revolution becomes shorter.

3. Which graph best illustrates the relationship between the period of revolution and gravitational force? Explain your answer. Graph 1. Increased gravitational force causes the period of revolution to decrease.

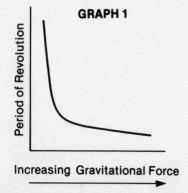

GRAPH 1

Period of Revolution

Increasing Gravitational Force

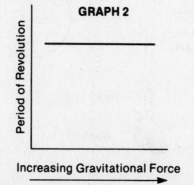

GRAPH 2

Period of Revolution

Increasing Gravitational Force

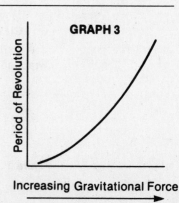

GRAPH 3

Period of Revolution

Increasing Gravitational Force

Critical Thinking and Application

1. Relate what you have learned in this investigation to the periods of revolution of the nine

   planets around the sun. The closer a planet is to the sun, the greater the pull of the sun's gravity on

   the planet, and the shorter the planet's period of revolution.

   _____

   _____

   _____

2. If an orbiting artificial satellite were to slow down, what would happen?

   Gravitational force would pull it back to the Earth. This occurs when an orbit decays and the satellite

   reenters the atmosphere.

3. Can you think of other types of motion in which the speed of an object increases as the

   force exerted on it increases? Answers may vary. The most obvious example is linear motion, in

   which the acceleration of an object is directly proportional to the force exerted on the object (F = ma).

   _____

   _____

   _____

Going Further

1. Investigate how a change in mass or distance affects the period of revolution of a ball. Repeat the investigation but keep the number of washers constant and change the mass of the Styrofoam ball. How does the mass of the orbiting object affect the period of revolution?

2. Try the same experiment but change the length of the fishing line.

Laboratory Investigation

Relating Distance and Apparent Motion

You may want to refer students to pages M60–M63 in their textbook for a general discussion of planetary motion.

Time required: 35 minutes

Background Information

When observing an object as it moves past you, there are two factors that affect its apparent motion, or how you perceive it. The first factor is the speed of the object. Its speed is visible to you, and you call it fast or slow in relation to other reference objects. The second factor that affects the apparent motion of an object is its distance from you and from the objects around it.

In this investigation you will examine how the distance of each planet from the Earth affects its apparent movement in the sky as observed from the Earth.

Problem

How does distance affect the apparent motion of a planet in the sky?

Materials *(per group)*

tape
2 sheets of paper
scissors
meterstick

Procedure

1. Cut one sheet of paper in half lengthwise. Tape the two halves together end to end to make one long strip of paper. Tape the strip of paper to the baseboard of a wall of your classroom as shown in Figure 1. The paper represents distant space.

2. Cut out four circles from the second sheet of paper. Each circle should be 5 cm in diameter. Label the circles Planet A, Planet B, Planet C, and Planet Earth.

3. Mark a point on the right side of the paper taped to the wall. Label this point Starting point. From this point, measure 20 cm, 40 cm, 80 cm, and 100 cm in a straight line away from the wall. At 20 cm, place Planet C on the floor. At 40 cm, place Planet B on the floor. At 80 cm, place Planet A on the floor. At 100 cm, place Planet Earth on the floor.

4. Move planets A, B, and C exactly 10 cm to the left, parallel to the wall. This represents the actual motion of the planets. Leave Planet Earth in its original location.

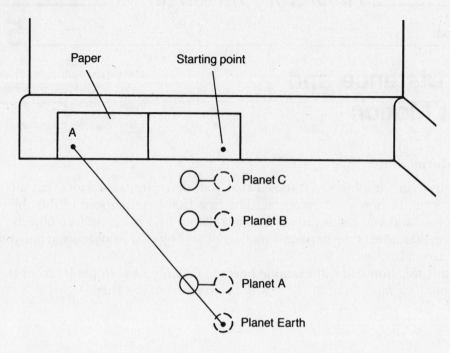

Paper   Starting point

A

Planet C

Planet B

Planet A

Planet Earth

Figure 1

5. With a meterstick, mark the point on the paper taped to the wall at which a straight line running from the center of Planet Earth through the center of Planet A would meet the paper. See Figure 1. Repeat this procedure for Planets B and C. Label the appropriate points A, B, and C on the paper.

6. Measure the distances from the starting point on the paper taped to the wall to the new points marked on the paper. Write each distance on the paper next to the measured line. Record these distances in the appropriate column of the Data Table.

Observations

DATA TABLE

Planet	Actual Distance Moved	Apparent Distance Moved
A	10 cm	Answers will vary.
B	10 cm	Answers will vary.
C	10 cm	Answers will vary.

Analysis and Conclusions

1. Which planet appeared to move the farthest? <u>Planet A.</u>

   Which planet appeared to move the least? <u>Planet C.</u>

2. How does the apparent motion of these planets compare with their actual motion?

   <u>The apparent motion of the planets is greater than their actual motion.</u>

   _____

   _____

   _____

3. How does the distance of an observer from an object affect the apparent motion of the

   object as seen by the observer? <u>Objects closer to the observer appear to move a greater distance</u>

   <u>than objects farther from the observer.</u>

   _____

   _____

   _____

Critical Thinking and Application

1. Why do you think the apparent motion of the planets is different from their actual motion?

   <u>Answers will vary but should include such ideas as parallax, angle of observation, and rotation of the</u>

   <u>Earth.</u>

   _____

   _____

   _____

2. If Planet C moved twice as far during the same time, how would its motion appear

   relative to Planet A? <u>Planet C would still appear to be moving more slowly than Planet A.</u>

   _____

   _____

   _____

3. Why is the motion of the planets in this investigation called "apparent motion"?

Because the observed motion is different from the actual motion. It is the motion as it "appears" to the

observer.

_____

4. Why is it important to measure the distances of the four planets straight away from the

wall? The planets should start on the same line in order to compare the motion.

_____

_____

_____

5. Why is it important to move the planets parallel to the wall?

The motion would appear different if the planets did not all move parallel.

_____

_____

_____

Going Further

1. Explore what happens to the results of this investigation if twice the distance from the starting point (40, 80, 160, 200 cm) and twice the parallel motion (20 cm) are used.

2. Observe the motion of nearby and distant objects, such as cars, people, or airplanes. Describe how their distances from you affect their apparent motion. Which seem to move farther? Faster?

Name _____ Class _____ Date _____

Laboratory Investigation

6

Determining Acceleration Due to Gravity

You may want to refer students to pages M93–M94 in their textbook for a general discussion of acceleration and escape velocity.

Time required: Part A—20 minutes
Part B—20 minutes

Background Information

If air resistance is small, the rate at which a body falls is constant, regardless of its mass. The rate at which a body falls is determined by the gravitational force exerted on the body. On the surface of the Earth, acceleration due to gravity is close to 9.8 m/sec².

In this investigation you will determine acceleration due to gravity using two different methods.

Problem

How can acceleration due to gravity near the surface of the Earth be determined?

Materials (per group)

A weight or heavy objects such as books can be placed on the base of the ring stand to steady it.

string or wire about 1.5 m
   long
hooked weight, 500 g
watch or clock   If burettes are not available, use anything
burette   that can control the rate of drip. A container
pie plate   with spigot works well. **Note:** *A container with*
meterstick   *a spigot will be easier to clean out than a burette.*
ring stand with burette clamp

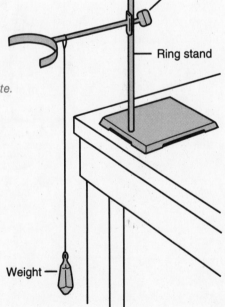

Burette clamp

Ring stand

Weight

Figure 1

Procedure

Part A Measuring Acceleration Due to Gravity
Using a Pendulum

1. Place the ring stand on a table so that the clamp hangs over the side of the table. See Figure 1. Tie one end of the string to the clamp. Attach the 500-g weight to the other end of the string.

© Prentice-Hall, Inc.

2. Measure the length (L) of the wire or string from the center of the weight to the ring stand. Record this length to the nearest 0.01 m in Data Table 1.

3. Pull the weight back about 10 degrees from its rest position. Release the weight and record in Data Table 1 the time (T) in seconds it takes to make 20 complete swings. One complete swing is back and forth.

Part B   Measuring the Acceleration of a Water Drop

1. Attach the burette to the ring stand with the burette clamp. See Figure 2. Fill the burette about three-quarters full of water.

2. Place the pie pan on the floor beneath the burette. The pie pan should be at least 1 m below the base of the burette.

3. Adjust the drip rate so that one drop just leaves the burette when the previous drop hits the pie pan. Watch the drop at the burette and listen for the sound.

4. Measure the distance (D) from the tip of the burette to the pie plate. Record this distance to the nearest 0.01 m in Data Table 2.

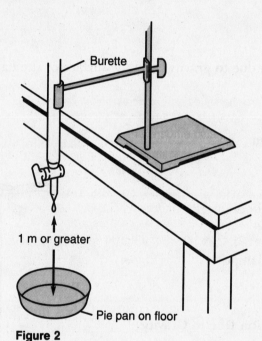

Figure 2

Observations
Part A

DATA TABLE 1

Length (L) (m)	Time (T) 20 swings (sec)
1.5 m	50 sec
(Approximate answers)	

1. Calculate the time (T) for a single swing. (Divide the time for 20 swings by 20.)

$$\frac{50 \text{ sec}}{20} = 2.5 \text{ sec}$$

2. Calculate the acceleration due to gravity in m/sec² using the following formula:

$$A_G = \frac{39.5 \times L}{T^2}$$

where A_G = acceleration of gravity, L = length in meters, and T = time in seconds for one swing.

$$A_G = \frac{(39.5 \times 1.5 \text{ m})}{(2.5 \text{ sec})^2} = 9.5 \text{ m/sec}^2$$

Part B

DATA TABLE 2

Distance (D) (m)	Time (T) 100 drops (sec)
1.0 m	46 sec
(Possible answers)	

3. Calculate the time (T) for a single water drop to fall. (Divide the time for 100 drops by 100.)

$$\frac{46 \text{ sec}}{100} = 0.46 \text{ sec}$$

4. Calculate the acceleration due to gravity using the following formula:

$$A_G = \frac{2D}{T^2}$$

where A_G = acceleration of gravity, D = distance in meters, and T = time in seconds for one drop.

$$A_G = \frac{2(1.0 \text{ m})}{(0.46 \text{ sec})^2} = 9.5 \text{ m/sec}^2$$

© Prentice-Hall, Inc.

Analysis and Conclusions

1. The acceleration of gravity is approximately 9.8 m/sec². Which method was more

   accurate? <u>Answers will vary.</u>

2. Suggest some possible reasons for your answer to question 1.

   <u>Answers will vary, but should reflect potential inaccuracies in measurement during either Part A or</u>

   <u>Part B.</u>

   _____

Critical Thinking and Application

1. Compare the motion of the object in Part A with the motion of the water droplets in Part B. How did the force of gravity influence each one?

   <u>The object in Part A moved in an arc, falling down then swinging back up. It was the force of gravity that</u>

   <u>pulled the object down to the low point of its arc each time. The water droplets fell to the ground in a</u>

   <u>straight line. It was the force of gravity that caused them to fall.</u>

   _____

   _____

2. Study the formula used to calculate acceleration due to gravity in Part A. Assuming that A_G is constant, what must be true about the relationship between the length of the string and the time it takes for the pendulum to make one complete swing?

   <u>The square of the time increases as the length of the string increases.</u>

   _____

   _____

3. Suppose you performed Part A using strings of varying lengths. How would you expect your calculated value of A_G to compare with the results you obtained in this investigation?

   <u>Should be the same.</u>

   _____

4. Study the formula you used to calculate acceleration due to gravity in Part B. How is the time taken for one droplet to fall related to the distance it falls?

   <u>The square of the time increases as the distance increases.</u>

   _____

Going Further

1. Perform Part A again, but this time attach a feather to the string instead of a weight.

   How does that affect your results? Why? Results no longer valid because of effects of air

   resistance on feather.

2. Perform Part B again, but this time use vegetable oil instead of water. How does that

   affect your results? No change.

_____ *Laboratory Investigation* _____

7 ____

Constructing a Foucault Pendulum

You may want to refer students to pages M104–M106 in their textbook for a general discussion of Earth's rotation.

Time required: 40 minutes

Background Information

In 1851, Jean Foucault performed an experiment that was the first proof that the Earth rotates. He hung a heavy iron ball from a wire that was 61 m long. Then he set it swinging like a pendulum in a north to south line. Foucault knew that a free-swinging pendulum does not change direction. However, after about 8 hours, the pendulum was swinging in an east to west line. Therefore, the Earth rotated beneath the swinging pendulum.

In this investigation you will make a device to help you understand the principle behind Foucault's pendulum.

Problem

How can you demonstrate that the Earth rotates?

Materials *(per group)*

2 ring stands	thread	fishing sinker or other
2 burette clamps	scissors	small heavy object,
wooden dowel about	sheet of lined paper	113 g or more in mass
30 cm long		

Procedure

1. Set up the ring stands and wooden dowel as pictured in Figure 1. Cut an appropriate length of thread. Tie the fishing sinker to one end of the thread. Tie the other end of the thread to the center of the wooden dowel so that the sinker can swing freely like a pendulum.

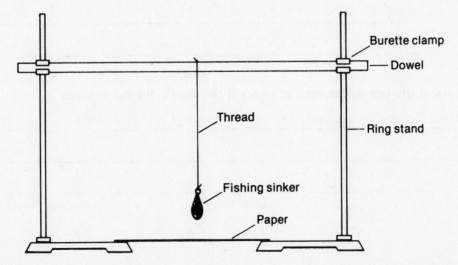

Figure 1

2. Tape a sheet of lined paper across the bases of the ring stands. The lines should be perpendicular to the direction of the dowel.

3. Several students in the group should position themselves on either side of the dowel. Another student should carefully set the pendulum swinging in the direction of the lines on the paper.

4. The students on either side of the dowel should slowly turn the whole apparatus clockwise one quarter of a full turn (90°).

5. Draw a two-headed arrow on the paper to show how the pendulum is now swinging. Label this arrow A. Observe how the direction of the pendulum has changed in relation to the students positioned on either side of the dowel.

6. The students on either side of the dowel should again slowly turn the whole apparatus clockwise another quarter of a turn (90°).

7. Draw another two-headed arrow on the paper to show how the pendulum is now swinging. Label this arrow B. Again observe how the direction of the pendulum has changed in relation to the students positioned on either side of the dowel.

Observations

1. Describe how the direction of arrow A differed from arrow B.

   Arrow A was perpendicular to arrow B.

2. Describe how the direction of the pendulum changed in relation to the students positioned on either side of the dowel. The pendulum does not change direction.

Analysis and Conclusions

1. If a pendulum were allowed to swing freely on the Earth, how would it appear to act if the Earth rotated? The pendulum would appear to slowly change direction opposite to the direction of the Earth's rotation.

2. How would the pendulum appear to act if the Earth did not rotate?

   The direction of the pendulum would appear not to change.

Critical Thinking and Application

1. Describe the changes in geographical direction that a pendulum would appear to undergo in 24 hours if it began swinging in a north to south line.

   After the first 6 hours, the pendulum would appear to swing east–west; after 12 hours back to

   north–south; after 18 hours back to east–west; and after 24 hours back to north–south.

2. What happens to the swing of a pendulum, or its arc, as the pendulum is allowed to

   swing over a period of time? The swing, or arc, gets smaller and smaller. Eventually the pendulum

   comes to a stop.

3. What is the reason for this change? Air resistance slows down the pendulum, eventually causing it

   to stop swinging.

Going Further

Construct a simple working model of Foucault's pendulum, as shown in Figure 2. Use a G-clamp with a ball bearing soldered to the inside of the jaw. Allow the ball bearing to rest on a flat, hard, and oiled metal surface. A heavy mass such as a large plastic bleach bottle filled with sand or water can then be hung from a 3-m cord. If carefully set in motion, this pendulum will appear to change direction with time. Where on the Earth would such a pendulum not change direction? North Pole and South Pole.

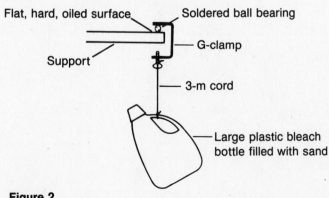

Flat, hard, oiled surface   Soldered ball bearing

Support

G-clamp

3-m cord

Large plastic bleach
bottle filled with sand

Figure 2

Critical Thinking and Application

1.

2.

3.

Going Further

_____ *Laboratory Investigation* _____

Earth and Its Moon   **8** _____

Comparing the Angle of Insolation and Temperature Changes

You may want to refer students to pages M107–M109 in their textbook for a general discussion of the relationship between Earth's tilted axis and the angle of the sun's rays.

Time required: 40 minutes

Background Information

The sun shines on each part of the Earth for the same total number of hours each year. However, there are areas of the Earth that receive more radiant energy from the sun than other areas do. Because the Earth's axis is tilted slightly and the Earth is a sphere, the sun's rays strike different areas of the Earth at different angles. The angle for a given area is called the angle of insolation.

In this investigation you will learn how the angle of the sun's rays affects temperature on the Earth.

Problem

How does the angle of insolation affect the rate of temperature change of a surface?

Materials *(per group)*

watch or clock
3 Celsius thermometers
high-wattage incandescent lamp
3 right triangular wooden blocks
   each with a 30°, a 60°, and a
   90° angle
masking tape

The wooden blocks can be cut in the industrial arts class a day before the class begins the investigation.

Procedure

1. Using masking tape, attach one thermometer to the 30° angle of one block. Then attach the second thermometer to the 60° angle of the second block and the third to the 90° angle of the last block. See Figure 1 on the next page.

2. Place the blocks, with the thermometers attached, as shown in Figure 1. Position the lamp so that it is 20 cm from the bulb of each thermometer. This means that the blocks will be positioned along the arc of a circle having a 20-cm radius.

3. Switch on the light. Record the temperature of each thermometer every minute for 15 minutes in the Data Table.

4. After the 15-minute observation interval, switch off the light.

5. Graph your data on the graph provided. Use the key given for each of the angles.

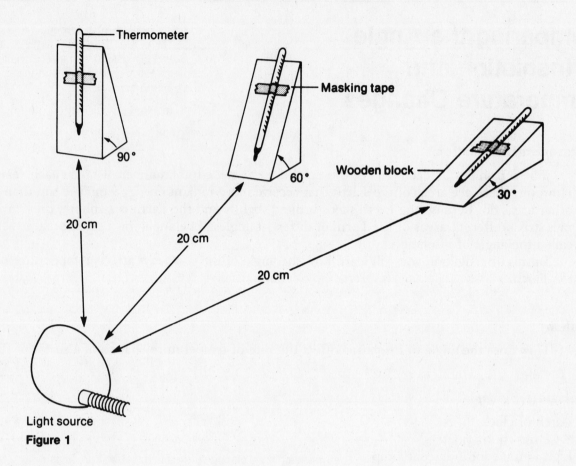

Figure 1

Observations

DATA TABLE Answers will vary.

Angle	Time (min)	0	1	2	3	4	5	6	7	8	9	10	11	12	13	14	15
30°	Temperature																
60°	Temperature																
90°	Temperature																

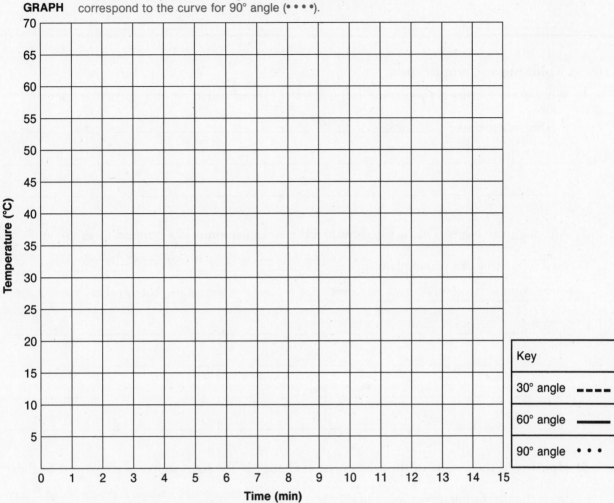

Graphs will vary depending on data, but the greatest
increase in temperature during the 15-minute interval should
correspond to the curve for 90° angle (• • • •).

GRAPH

Key

30° angle	----
60° angle	——
90° angle	• • •

Analysis and Conclusions

1. Which angle caused the temperature to increase the most during the 15 minutes? What region of the Earth receives sunlight at this angle?

   90°. The equator is where the sun's rays are perpendicular to the Earth.

2. Which angle caused the temperature to increase the least during the 15 minutes? What region of the Earth receives sunlight at this angle?

   30°. The far northern and southern latitudes.

3. What is the relationship between the size of the angle of insolation and the surface

temperature? As the angle of insolation decreases, the rate of increase in surface temperature also

decreases.

Critical Thinking and Application

1. What other factors do you think influence the rate of warming of a particular spot on

the Earth's surface? Time of day and season.

2. Although the North Pole is tilted toward the sun in summer, its temperatures are still

very cold. How can you explain this? The angle of insolation is still very small. The summer

temperatures at the North Pole will be warmer than the winter temperatures, but there are never enough

direct rays of the sun to make the North Pole very warm.

3. How would the results of this investigation change if the light source were placed farther

from the thermometers? Closer to them? The graph of temperature change over time for each

angle would show essentially the same shape, but the overall temperatures would be lower for a more

distant light source and higher for a closer light source.

Going Further

   Test different soils to determine what effect soils have on the rate of heating. Prepare
mounds of different types of soil. Use a protractor to be sure the angles of the mounds are
the same. Place a thermometer on each mound. Keep a record of the temperature each
minute for 15 minutes. Draw a graph to compare the temperature versus time for each soil.

Name _____ Class _____ Date _____

_____ *Laboratory Investigation* _____

Earth and Its Moon

9

Models of Eclipses

You may want to refer students to pages M121–M123 in their textbook for a general discussion of lunar and solar eclipses.

Time required: 25 minutes

Background Information

As the moon and the Earth revolve around each other and the sun, they block some of the sun's light. When the sun or moon is blocked out by another object, an eclipse occurs. There are two types of eclipses—a lunar eclipse and a solar eclipse. During a lunar eclipse, the moon passes through the Earth's shadow. A solar eclipse occurs when the moon is directly between the sun and the Earth.

Shadows cast into space during an eclipse have two parts. The completely dark inner shadow is the umbra. The outer area where light is only partially blocked is called the penumbra.

In this investigation you will draw a model of a solar eclipse and of a lunar eclipse and identify the parts of a shadow.

Problem

What happens during a solar and a lunar eclipse? What are the parts of the shadows they form?

Materials *(per student)*

metric ruler
colored pencils

Procedure

1. Each step of the procedure should be done on the appropriate figure in Observations.

2. Color the sun orange, the moon blue, and the Earth green in both Figures 1 and 2.

3. On Figure 1, use the ruler to draw a line from each side of the sun to the same side of the moon. Extend these lines until they intersect with the Earth. Use the diagram below as a guide.

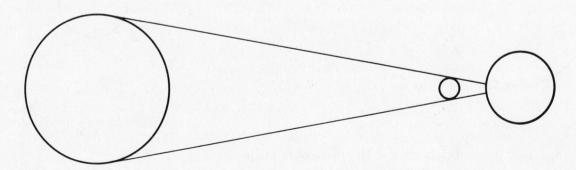

4. On the same figure, use the ruler to draw lines from the same points on the sides of the sun to the opposite sides of the moon. Extend these lines until they intersect with the Earth. Use the diagram below as a guide.

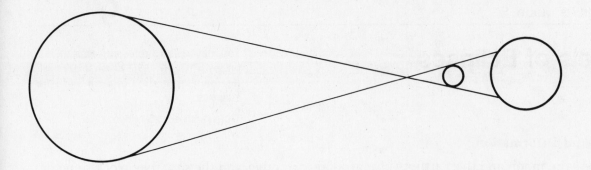

5. Color the umbra black and the penumbra purple.

6. On Figure 2, use the ruler to draw a line from each side of the sun to the same side of the Earth. Extend these lines 4 cm beyond the Earth. Use the diagram below as a guide.

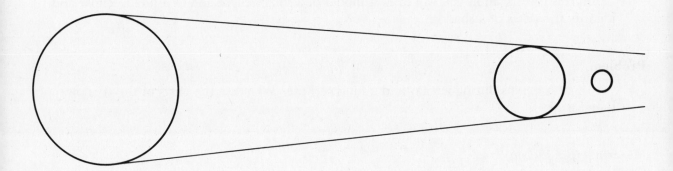

7. On the same figure, use the ruler to draw lines from the sides of the sun to the opposite sides of the Earth. Extend these lines 4 cm beyond the Earth. Use the diagram below as a guide.

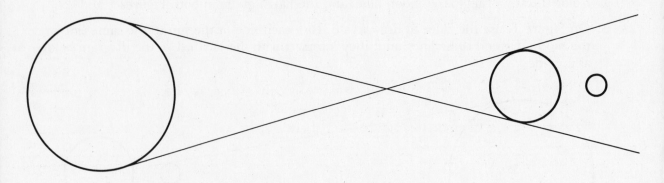

8. Color the umbra black and the penumbra purple.

Observations

Eclipses

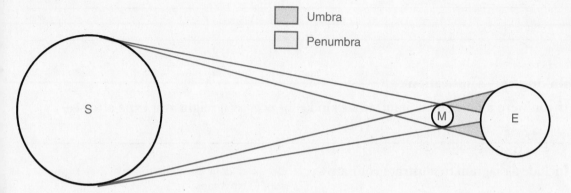

Umbra
Penumbra

Figure 1

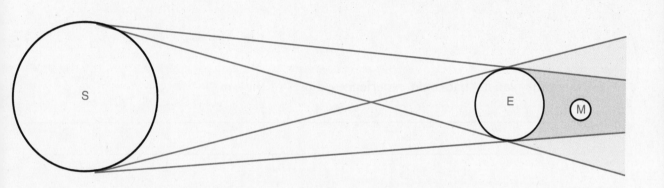

Figure 2

Analysis and Conclusions

1. What type of eclipse have you drawn in Figure 1?

   Solar eclipse. _____

   In Figure 2? Lunar eclipse. _____

2. At what phase is the moon in Figure 1? New moon. _____

   In Figure 2? Full moon. _____

3. Which type of eclipse occurs with the greatest frequency?

   Partial lunar eclipse. _____

4. Explain why a total solar eclipse or total lunar eclipse does not occur at least once a

month. The moon revolves around the Earth in a slightly tilted orbit. Therefore, the alignment of the

sun, moon, and Earth required for a total solar eclipse or total lunar eclipse rarely occurs.

Critical Thinking and Application

1. a. If you were a lunar inhabitant, what kind(s) of eclipse(s) might you expect to see?

Eclipse of the sun (sun, Earth, moon).

b. Include a diagram to illustrate your answer. Check student diagrams to make sure order is
sun, Earth, moon.

2. Name the planets that could experience eclipses of the sun.

Earth, Mars, Jupiter, Saturn, Uranus, Neptune, Pluto.

3. Why does our moon, which is much smaller than our sun, produce a total eclipse of the

sun? Even though it is much smaller than the sun, the moon can produce a total solar eclipse because

its relative nearness to the Earth makes it large enough to block all the light from the sun.

Going Further

Using a light source and balls of different sizes, construct models of solar and lunar
eclipses. This activity also makes a good teacher demonstration.